Downs and Ups
at Daisy Hill School

The life of Jesus for young readers

by Brian Ogden

Text copyright © Brian Ogden 2000
Illustrations copyright © Simon Smith 2000

The author asserts the moral right to be
identified as the author of this work.

Published by
The Bible Reading Fellowship
Peter's Way, Sandy Lane West
Oxford OX4 5HG

ISBN 1 84101 116 9

First edition 2000

10 9 8 7 6 5 4 3 2 1 0

Acknowledgments
Scripture quotations are taken from the
Good News Bible published by The Bible
Societies/HarperCollins Publishers Ltd UK
© American Bible Society, 1966, 1971,
1976, 1992.
p.35 Material from the *Alternative Service
Book 1980* is copyright © The Archbishops'
Council and is reproduced by permission.

A catalogue record for this book is
available from the British Library.

Printed and bound in Great Britain
by Caledonian International Book
Manufacturing , Glasgow.

Introduction

'He came down to earth from heaven,' reads one of the Christmas carols. This book looks at the life of Jesus from 'coming down to earth' to the time when the friends of Jesus saw him taken up to heaven.

It is a life of Christ told within the setting of Daisy Hill Primary School. In this book we meet Mrs Hazel and her class, 2H, who help us, through their work, to follow the life of Jesus from his birth to his ascension. In the school is Mrs Jolley and her Reception class, whom you can meet in the *On the Story Mat* books, and Mr Green with 3G from the *Just Time to Catch the Post* books. You can find your way round the school by looking at the Daisy Hill picture map on page 4.

This is a book which can be given to individual children. But it can also be used in school as a part of a class or whole-school teaching or assembly programme on the life of Jesus, or with a church-based group. It presents the life of Jesus as a consecutive whole rather than as separate stories. This aspect is emphasized by the use of the Big Frieze which grows as the story continues. In the book, the children participate in a number of ways. Teachers may find the suggestions to be useful in their own situations.

Daisy Hill County Primary School Picture Map

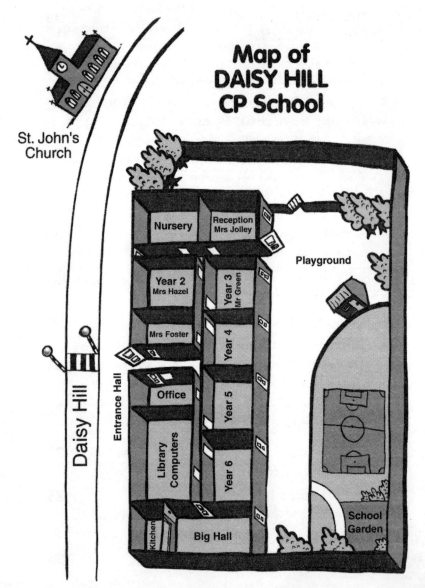

St. John's Church

Map of DAISY HILL CP School

Nursery

Reception Mrs Jolley

Playground

Year 2 Mrs Hazel

Year 3 Mr Green

Mrs Foster

Year 4

Daisy Hill

Entrance Hall

Office

Year 5

Library Computers

Year 6

Kitchen

Big Hall

School Garden

Contents

The story starts here...

In Class Two, Mrs Hazel's children were sitting in the story corner. Some were sitting more sensibly than others. Eleanor was trying to push Steven off the beanbag. Mrs Hazel came and sat in her chair. She looked at Eleanor. Eleanor slid down on to the floor.

'That's better,' said Mrs Hazel. 'Now we can start.'

Mrs Hazel picked up a book from beside her chair. On the front of the book were the words 'Family Album'.

'I've borrowed this book from my mother to show you. It's called a Family Album. My mother has put lots of photographs in here. Let's have a look at a page.'

Mrs Hazel showed 2H a photograph of a little girl playing on a beach. Underneath was a date and the place where the photograph was taken.

'I wonder if you can guess who this is?' asked Mrs Hazel.

All the children looked hard at the picture. 'I think it's you!' said Suzi.

'Quite right,' said Mrs Hazel, with a smile. 'It's a photo of me when I was four. This book is full of photos. There are some when I went to school, some when I was at college, some of my wedding and some now of my children. It's really a book of my life that my mother has put together.'

'Can we see you getting wedded?' asked Kerry. 'We say "getting married",' said Mrs Hazel, as she turned the pages. She showed the children the picture taken outside the church on her wedding day.

'You looked younger then!' said Jack.

'Thank you, Jack!' said Mrs Hazel.

Mrs Hazel shut the book and put it down.

'Our new topic is about the life of Jesus,' said Mrs Hazel. 'We can't have photos like in my Family Album. But we can have lots of pictures painted by you. I think it would be fun to have a long frieze around the wall. We can tell the story of Jesus' life on the frieze. We'll call it our Big Frieze.'

'We've got one of them at home,' said Eleanor. 'We keep our lollies in it!'

'This one goes on the wall,' said Mrs Hazel, smiling. 'It's a frieze, not a freezer. You can take it in turns to paint the pictures for it. Sometimes we shall act the story as well. In fact, Mrs Foster has asked us to act the first part of the story. This will be for the assembly next week in the Big Hall.'

The children loved drama and they all wanted to be in the play.

'Kerry, I want you to be Mary,' said Mrs Hazel. 'Thomas, you can be Joseph and Steven will be the angel.'

All week they practised hard.

1. Messages

It was Wednesday morning at Daisy Hill Primary School. On Wednesdays, all the children came together in the Big Hall for assembly.

Mrs Foster, the head teacher, stopped the music.

'Good morning, everyone,' she said.

'Today we are starting a new story. The story is all about one person. The story is all about Jesus. A good place to start a story is at the beginning. Mrs Hazel's class are going to show us how the story begins.'

'Our story starts with Mary, Joseph and an angel,' said Mrs Hazel. 'Mary and Joseph lived in a town called Nazareth a long time ago. Mary worked hard, cleaning her house.'

Mary came on, sweeping the floor.

'One day, she had a visitor. It was an angel. Mary was very surprised to see an angel,' said Mrs Hazel. 'I expect you would be, too. The angel told Mary not to be afraid. Mary knew that angels were God's messengers. Perhaps the angel had a message for her.

"God has been gracious to you," said the angel. "You will give birth to a son, and you will name him Jesus. He will be great. He will be called the Son of the Most High God."

"I am God's servant," said Mary.'

'So Mary was told that she would have a very special baby,' said Mrs Hazel. 'Mary was engaged to a man called Joseph. She was going to marry Joseph quite soon.'

Joseph came through the door into the hall. He was carrying a hammer and a piece of wood.

'Joseph was a carpenter in Nazareth,' said Mrs Hazel. 'He made chairs and tables. He made doors and windows. He mended fences so that animals didn't run away. Joseph was a very busy carpenter.'

Joseph pretended to knock a nail into the piece of wood. Just as Joseph pretended to hit his thumb, Mary came back. She looked at Joseph and laughed.

'Mary,' said Mrs Hazel, 'told Joseph about

the angel. She told him that she was going to have a baby and that the baby was to be God's son.'

After Mary had gone, Joseph pretended to go to sleep. The angel came and stood by Joseph.

'When Joseph was asleep,' said Mrs Hazel, 'an angel came to Joseph in a dream. The angel told Joseph that he should marry Mary. He also told Joseph that Mary would have a son.'

The angel went away and Joseph woke up. He fetched Mary and they stood together at the front.

'Joseph and Mary got married,' said Mrs Hazel. 'Mary started to get things ready for her baby. I think Joseph did, too. Mary did a lovely thing before the baby was born. She made up a beautiful poem. Donna is going to read some of the verses.'

Donna opened the big class Bible. 'This is what Mary wrote,' said Donna.

'My heart praises the Lord;
    my soul is glad because of God my Saviour,
    for he has remembered me,
    his lowly servant!
From now on all people will call me happy,
    because of the great things
    the Mighty God has done for me.'

'Thank you, Donna,' said Mrs Foster, 'and a big thank you as well to Kerry, Steven and Thomas and to Mrs Hazel. They have helped us to start our story about Jesus. Now I'm going to say a prayer.'

Loving Father, thank you that we can learn about the life of your son, Jesus. Please help us to get to know him better. Amen

After the prayer, the children went back to their classrooms.

'Well done,' said Mrs Hazel. 'I'm very proud of you.'

Look hard and you can see the picture that Jack and Kerry painted for the Big Frieze.

2. Mary's baby

'Yesterday in class,' said Mrs Hazel, 'we thought about the time when Jesus was born. We talked about the journey that Joseph and Mary had to make. We heard about the people who came to see him. When we finished everyone wrote their own stories. Now we're going to put all the stories together. Steven, please will you start?'

'Mary and Joseph were at home,' said Steven. 'A soldier came to Nazareth where they lived. The soldier told them that they had to go to their own cities.'

'Yes, Joseph and Mary had to go to their own city,' said Mrs Hazel. 'But Mary was going to have a baby, so they had to travel very slowly. Do you remember the name of the city?'

'It was Bethlehem,' said Steven.

'Thank you, Steven,' said Mrs Hazel. 'Yes, Mary and Joseph and all their friends had to make a long journey. Eleanor, tell us what happened next, please.'

'Bethlehem was full of people,' said Eleanor. 'All the hotels and pubs were full up. Joseph couldn't find anywhere for them to stay.'

'Joseph knocked on lots of doors,' said Mrs Hazel. 'But at last a kind man said, "You can have my..." What?'

Everyone's hand went up.

'Stable,' said Kerry.

'Yes. I think he told Joseph that there was plenty of hay in the stable to keep the baby warm,' said Mrs Hazel. 'So baby Jesus was born in a stable. I think Mary and Joseph were very happy. But soon they had some visitors. Mark, tell us about them, please.'

'Near Bethlehem,' said Mark, 'there were some hills. On the hills were lots of sheep. Some shepherds looked after the sheep. One night, something happened.'

'Something very unusual happened,' said Mrs Hazel. 'Can you tell me what it was?'

'Well,' said Mark, 'some angels came. They sang a song. I think it woke all the sheep. One of the angels told the shepherds to go down to Bethlehem 'cos a special baby was born.'

'Good,' said Mrs Hazel. 'I think the shepherds left their sheep and ran down the hill to find the baby. The shepherds were very excited. Kerry, tell us what they found, please.'

'They ran until they got to the stable,' said Kerry. 'Joseph and Mary were a bit surprised to see them. But the shepherds were very quiet and the baby never woke up. I think they might have taken him a present.'

'Well done,' said Mrs Hazel. 'I expect they were very excited after seeing the baby Jesus. They went back up the hill shouting and singing. The shepherds were the first people to see Jesus, apart from Joseph and Mary. Later on, Jesus had some rather unusual visitors. I know you wrote about them, Jack.'

'When Jesus was a little bit older,' said Jack, 'some clever men came to see him. We know they were clever because we sometimes call them the wise men. They had come a long way.'

'They had come a very long way,' said Mrs Hazel. 'The wise men had followed a very bright star. It led them right to Bethlehem.

When they found Jesus, they gave him three presents. Can anyone remember what those presents were?'

'There was gold,' said Thomas.

'I think it's something like frankincense,' said Eleanor.

'And myrrh,' said Suzi.

'Well done, everybody,' said Mrs Hazel. 'You've really worked hard. Now, after we've said our prayer, I've got a surprise for you.'

Father God, thank you that Jesus came to live with us at the first Christmas. Thank you that, although we can't see him, he still lives with us today. Amen

'What's the surprise?' asked Donna.

'Mrs Jolley has asked us if we will tell our stories to her children in Reception,' said Mrs Hazel.

The next day, Mrs Jolley and her children listened hard to the stories.

'Well done,' said Mrs Jolley.

Mrs Jolley's children gave 2H a big clap.

Later, all the children made a lovely picture of the angel and shepherds and sheep. They added this to the Big Frieze.

3. Not lost—just missing

The children in 2H and Mrs Hazel were
sitting in the story corner.

'One day, when my son Martin was little,'
said Mrs Hazel, 'he got lost in the
supermarket. I thought Martin was with my
husband. My husband thought Martin was
with me. Then we realized Martin was
missing. We were very worried.'

'I bet he was by the sweets,' said Eleanor.
'My brother would be!'

'You're right, Eleanor,' said Mrs Hazel.
'He was. He didn't seem worried that he
couldn't see us.'

'Did you get him some sweets?' asked Thomas.

'Yes, we did. We were so pleased to have found him. I gave Martin a great big "I've found you" hug.'

'That's a nice story,' said Donna. 'I like "lost and found" stories.'

'Something like that happened to Jesus,' said Mrs Hazel. 'When he was twelve he went with his parents from Nazareth to Jerusalem. That was a bit like us going from Daisy Hill to London—from a small town to a very large city. Jesus went to the big church, or temple, in Jerusalem.'

Mrs Hazel held up a big picture of the temple in Jerusalem.

'This was where Jesus went,' said Mrs Hazel. 'It must have been very exciting for him. Jesus loved it.'

'I s'pose Mary went shopping,' said Steven. 'That's what my mum would do!'

'I don't know about that,' said Mrs Hazel, smiling. 'We know that Jesus spent a long time in the temple. Soon they had to go back home. In those days, people travelled in big groups. It was safer. The women and children left first. They walked more slowly.

The men started later. They caught up with
the women by the evening. But when
Joseph met Mary, someone was missing.
Who was that?'

'Jesus!' said all the children together.

'Yes, Jesus was missing,' said Mrs Hazel. 'Joseph and Mary searched for Jesus everywhere. Nobody had seen Jesus at all.'

'That's like you when you lost Martin,' said Donna.

'Yes, it was,' said Mrs Hazel. 'Mary and Joseph did the only thing they could. What do you think that was?'

'Went back to the big city,' said Steven.

'Well done,' said Mrs Hazel. 'Mary and Joseph hurried back to Jerusalem. Soon they were back in the big city. Where do you think Jesus was?'

'Where they stayed,' said Kerry.

'By the shops,' said Mark.

'In the big church,' said Thomas.

'Thomas is right,' said Mrs Hazel. 'Jesus was in the big church—the temple. Mary and Joseph found him there. They had been looking for him for three days.'

'What was he doing in the temple?' asked Suzi. 'Wasn't it a bit boring?'

'I don't think Jesus thought so,' said Mrs Hazel, quietly. 'Jesus was listening to some clever men. Mary and Joseph were surprised to find him there. Let's see what the Bible tells us about it.'

Mrs Hazel asked Kerry to read these verses.
'His mother said to him, "My son, why
have you done this to us? Your father and I
have been terribly worried trying to find
you." Jesus answered them, "Why did you
have to look for me? Didn't you know that I
had to be in my Father's house?"'

'Thank you, Kerry,' said Mrs Hazel. 'Jesus
was saying that he was in God's house—the
temple. He was reminding Mary and Joseph
that he wasn't just their son, but God's son,
too. It was a very special time for them all.'

'I think Mary gave him a big "I've found you" hug, too,' said Eleanor.

'I'm sure she did. Now we'll be quiet for a moment and have our prayer.'

Loving Father, we know you are the father of Jesus. Help us to remember that you are our father, too. Amen

'Steven and Donna, it's your turn to paint the picture for our Big Frieze, please,' said Mrs Hazel.

4. Promises

St John the Baptist church is very near Daisy Hill School. The children in 2H can see the church from their classroom. The vicar of the church is an old friend of Daisy Hill School.

If you look at the picture map at the beginning of this book, you can find the church.

As the children walked up the church path, they saw the vicar waiting for them. They all sat down at the back of the church.

'Welcome to St John's,' said the vicar. 'It's
really good to see you here. Some of you
know our church and come to our services.
Some of you were baptized here. I
remember Mark's and Kerry's baptisms. Can
anyone tell me where we baptize people in
this church?'

'In the font,' said Suzi.

At the back of the church there was a big
stone font. The children came and stood
around the font.

'This is where I baptized Mark and Kerry,' said the vicar. 'Mark was a baby—only a few months old. Often, though, people are baptized when they are older. We had a lovely service last year. Kerry's mum and dad and Kerry herself were all baptized together.'

The vicar picked up a big doll.

'Look,' he said, 'I've borrowed my daughter's doll to show you how we baptize babies. But we need a name for her. What do you think we should call her?'

'Emma,' said Donna.

'That's a good name,' said the vicar.

There was some water in the font. The vicar stood by the font, holding Emma.

'Emma—I baptize you in the name of the Father, and of the Son, and of the Holy Spirit.'

The vicar dipped his fingers into the water. He made the sign of the cross with the water on Emma's forehead.

'The baptism service is very special,' said the vicar. 'The person being baptized is welcomed into God's family in the service. Some very important promises are made about following Jesus. Now I want to show you something else.'

The children followed the vicar and sat down in the choir seats.

'Look at the big window.'

Right at the eastern end of the church was a huge window made from coloured glass.

'Can anyone tell me about the picture?' asked the vicar.

The children looked hard. There were two people standing in a river. One was wearing a rough, woolly coat. The other one seemed to have a bird flying just above his head.

'I think it's Jesus,' said Thomas.

'And who is standing next to him?' asked the vicar.

'Is it John?' asked Kerry. 'John the Baptist?'

'Well done,' said the vicar. 'Our church is named after John the Baptist. This is a picture of John baptizing Jesus. But this didn't happen in a font! John baptized Jesus in the River Jordan.

It was a very special time for Jesus. He left home in Nazareth and went to John to be baptized. After that, Jesus started to tell everyone about God, his Father.'

'But what's that bird doing?' asked Jack.

'The bird is a dove,' said the vicar. 'We often show the Holy Spirit as a dove. God sent his Holy Spirit to help Jesus tell everyone about God.'

'Thank you very much,' said Mrs Hazel. 'Now we can add some more pictures to our Big Frieze. Before we go, we'll ask the vicar to say our prayer.'

'I'm going to say a part of the prayer we use in the baptism service,' said the vicar. 'It reminds us that we all belong to God's family.'

Heavenly Father,
in your love you have called us to know you,
led us to trust you,
and bound our life with yours.
Surround us with your love;
protect us from evil;
fill us with your Holy Spirit. Amen

'Just before we go, look hard at that window,' said Mrs Hazel. 'I'd like everyone to draw a picture of it when we get back to school. Then we can choose one to put on our Big Frieze.'

5. There's people to be caught

It was Wednesday morning and 2H were sitting in the Big Hall for the assembly. When all the classes had come in, Mrs Foster, the head teacher, spoke.

'Every class has been thinking about the life of Jesus. This morning, 3G are going to tell us about some of the people who became friends of Jesus. I'm going to ask Mr Green if he will introduce some of these people to you.'

'When Jesus was on earth,' said Mr Green, 'he made many friends. Some of them were special friends called disciples. These were the ones who spent a lot of time with Jesus. Jesus taught them about God so that they could teach other people. We are going to meet some of Jesus' friends this morning.'

Two boys walked on. They were holding a long piece of string. The string was stretched between them. Hanging from the string were lots of paper fish.

'My name's Simon Peter and this is my brother. His name is Andrew.

As you can see, we're both fishermen.'

The two boys pulled the string and the fish jumped up and down.

'One day, we were fishing in Lake Galilee. Suddenly someone came close to the water's edge and spoke to us. It was Jesus. "Come with me, and I will teach you to catch people," he said.

It may sound very strange to you, but that's what we did. We left our boat and our nets and we followed Jesus.

We had lots of adventures with Jesus. We became very close friends and for three years we went everywhere with him. And yes, we did catch people.'

The boys put down their string with the fish. They picked up another one which had paper people hanging from it.

'But Simon Peter and Andrew weren't the only people on the beach when Jesus came

along,' said Mr Green. 'Further along the shore were two more brothers. Their names were James and John. Their father had a lovely name—his name was Zebedee.'

Two more boys from 3G came on. They were holding a big cut-out cardboard boat in front of them.

'We were in our father's boat. James and I were getting the nets ready for a night's fishing.

We saw our friends Simon Peter and Andrew walking along the beach towards us. Jesus was with them. Jesus spoke to us. "Come with me, and I will teach you to catch people," said Jesus.'

The boys left their boat leaning against a chair. They shared the people-string with Simon Peter and Andrew. The four boys then walked off together with the string.

'Jesus had lots of friends then,' said Mr Green. 'But he's got even more today.'

'Thank you, Mr Green, and all of 3G,' said Mrs Foster. 'That was a very good way of telling us more about the life of Jesus. Now we'll have our prayer.'

Jesus, friend and brother, thank you for all your friends in the Bible. Help us to know your friendship, too, and help us to be friends to everyone. Amen

Back in their classroom, 2H talked about the friends of Jesus. Thomas and Donna painted the big picture for the Big Frieze. It showed Jesus by the lake with Simon Peter and his brother Andrew.

6. Ear today and gone tomorrow!

Daisy Hill School has a large playing field. Just beyond the football pitch is the school garden. Some children belong to the Gardening Club which Mrs Hazel runs at lunchtime. Every year, they plan what seeds they are going to sow. Then they dig and rake the ground, ready for the seeds.

If you look at the picture map at the beginning of this book, you can find the garden.

'Some of you,' said Mrs Hazel to 2H, 'belong to the Gardening Club. Two months ago, we sowed some seeds. Since then, the sun has shone and we've also had plenty of rain. Donna, tell everyone what's happening, please.'

'The seeds have come up,' said Donna. 'Well, most of them have.'

'Now, since it's such a lovely day, we're all going down to look at the school garden,' said Mrs Hazel.

All the children in 2H followed Mrs Hazel across the field, down to the garden. They stood round the path.

'We sowed the seed the same way it was sown in Jesus' time,' said Mrs Hazel. 'Mark, tell us how you did it, please.'

'I took a handful of seed,' said Mark, 'and walked up and down. As I walked, I threw some seed on the ground.'

'Do you remember what the weather was like?' asked Mrs Hazel.

'It was rather windy,' said Mark. 'Some of the seed blew away.'

'Now let's see what we can find,' said Mrs Hazel. 'Some of the seed fell on this concrete path. Do you think it grew?'

'No,' said Eleanor. 'You can't grow things in concrete.'

'Some of the seed fell on that rough ground over there,' said Mrs Hazel. 'There's not much earth for it to grow in. Jack, you're the nearest. Can you see any plants?'

'Well, there's sort of dead things,' said Jack. 'It looks like they started and then just died.'

'That was when we had those very hot days last week,' said Mrs Hazel. 'You see, there wasn't enough moisture in the soil. The sun just scorched them.'

'These things are just weeds,' said Eleanor, pointing to a patch of plants. 'My grandad doesn't like weeds!'

'Yes,' said Mrs Hazel. 'We haven't got round to digging that patch yet. But you know, some of our seeds blew into those weeds. I don't think they had much chance to grow well. The weeds have smothered them.'

'But lots of our seeds have grown,' said Donna. 'Where we dug it properly, they've done really well.'

Back in the classroom, Mrs Hazel read the children a story. It was a story called the Parable of the Sower.

'But that's just what we've seen!' said Thomas. 'It was like the school garden.'

'That's right,' said Mrs Hazel. 'You see, one day Jesus was talking to a crowd of people. I think he could see a man in the fields, sowing seed. The man sowed his seed the same way Mark sowed ours. Jesus told the people this story. It was one of the stories Jesus told that we call parables. Jesus used parables to teach about God. We enjoy the stories, but we have to think about what they mean.'

'Can Donna and I paint the Big Frieze picture?' asked Mark.

'In a few moments,' said Mrs Hazel. 'But first let's talk about the story. I think Jesus was saying that people hear what he says in different ways. Some, like the seeds on the

concrete, don't listen at all. Some, like the rough ground, listen but soon forget.

Some are like the weedy patch. They listen to Jesus but then lots of other things come along and they don't listen any more. Some, like the good ground, listen and take notice and follow Jesus.

Now let's have our prayer.'

Loving Father, you have given us ears to hear. Help us to listen to our friends when they speak, but most of all, help us to listen to you. Amen

'Now, Mark and Donna, you can paint our Big Frieze picture for us.'

'Please, Mrs Hazel, can we join the Gardening Club?' asked Thomas and Suzi.

7. Now open your eyes

It was Wednesday morning and 2H went into assembly. They were rather surprised to see a dog sitting at the front. He was wearing a harness. Holding the lead at the other end of the harness was a lady.

'Today, as you can see,' said Mrs Foster, 'we have a special visitor. In fact, we have two special visitors. I'd like to welcome Mrs Parsons and her friend, Toby. Mrs Parsons has come to speak to us and will, I'm sure, tell you about Toby.'

Mrs Parsons stood up and Toby lay down and went to sleep.

'Thank you, Mrs Foster, for your welcome to Daisy Hill,' she said.

'Toby and I are very pleased to be here. Some of you will have guessed by now that I don't see very well. Toby has become my eyes. He takes me safely wherever I want to go. He helps me cross the road and he stops me bumping into lamp-posts.'

Mrs Parsons went on to tell the children about Guide Dogs for the Blind—how dogs are trained to help people who can't see. She told them about some of the adventures that she and Toby had had. She thanked them for the money which the school had sent to help train more dogs.

When they were back in their classroom, Mrs Hazel spoke to 2H.

'This morning we've learnt a lot about people who can't see. When you can't see, it's not easy to find work. It's not easy to travel about. When Jesus lived on earth, it was even harder. Many people who couldn't see had no one to help them. One of these was a man called Bartimaeus.'

Mrs Hazel picked up a book.

'I'm going to tell you the story of how Bartimaeus met Jesus. It's written as though Bartimaeus is telling the story. Try to listen to the story with your eyes shut. Then you'll know what it was like for Bartimaeus.'

Mrs Hazel started to read.

'My name is Bartimaeus. I live in the city of Jericho. I had been blind for years. I spent my days sitting by the gate of the city, hoping people would give me money. One day there was a huge crowd. I could hear them but I couldn't see them. I asked what was happening. A kind man told me that Jesus was coming to Jericho.

The crowd were all waiting to see him. I knew he was getting nearer by what the crowd were saying.

"Jesus! Take pity on me," I shouted.

Some of the crowd told me to be quiet. I didn't take any notice of them.

"Jesus! Take pity on me," I shouted even louder.

Then something wonderful happened. Even with the noise of the crowd, Jesus heard me.

"Cheer up," said someone in the crowd. "Get up, he is calling you."

I jumped up and followed the voices. Then I knew I was standing in front of Jesus.

"What do you want me to do for you?" Jesus asked me.

"Teacher," I said, "I want to see again."

"Go," said Jesus, "your faith has made you well."

And I could see. I could really see. I could see again, thanks to Jesus.'

Mrs Hazel closed the book.

'Now open your eyes,' said Mrs Hazel. 'Now you can imagine how Bartimaeus felt when he could see. He was a very happy man. Jesus made lots of people well. Now, before we choose who will paint our Big Frieze picture, we'll have our prayer.'

Loving Father, thank you for making people well. Help all doctors and nurses as they try to make people well. Amen

'I think that it's Steven's and Kerry's turn to paint our picture.'

8. Two-way talking

Eleanor and Kerry were reading quietly. Steven, Mark, Suzi and Donna were doing some number sheets. Jack and Thomas were using the computer. Suddenly there was a very strange noise. It seemed to come from under Mrs Hazel's table. Mrs Hazel kept her handbag under her table.

The noise was quite loud. It made everyone jump. The noise didn't stop. A quiet classroom became a rather noisy one.

'Perhaps it's a bomb!' said Eleanor.

'I think it's a wild animal,' said Thomas.

'No!' said Donna.
'I know what it is.
It's a phone.'

'Oh dear,' said Mrs Hazel. 'Donna, I think you're right.'

She went to her table and picked up her bag. The noise was still going on. Mrs Hazel opened her bag and took out a mobile phone. It was ringing quite loudly now. She spoke into the phone and then listened. After a short while, she turned it off.

'I'm very sorry about that,' she said. 'My husband lent me his phone today so that I could tell him when to meet me after school. I forgot to turn it off.'

'My dad's got one like that,' said Steven.

'So's mine,' said some of the other children.

'Since I seem to have disturbed everyone, I think we'll have a change,' said Mrs Hazel. 'Please come and sit in the story corner.'

The children settled down. Eleanor got there first and grabbed the beanbag.

'We're going to think about the next part of our Big Frieze,' said Mrs Hazel. 'There was one thing that Jesus did every day. He talked to God, his Father. What do we call it when we talk to God?'

'Saying our prayers,' said Jack.

'That's right,' said Mrs Hazel. 'And Jesus often prayed to God, his Father. One day, when he had finished, one of his friends said to Jesus, "Lord, teach us to pray." It was then that Jesus taught his friends the prayer we call the Lord's Prayer.'

'I know,' said Suzi. 'It's the Our Father prayer.'

'That's right,' said Mrs Hazel. 'Jesus told us to start our prayers by saying "Our Father". We say that prayer in assembly sometimes. Let's see what else Jesus told his friends to say.'

Mrs Hazel opened the big class Bible and passed it to Thomas.

'Thomas, read these verses, please.'

'Jesus said, "When you pray, say this,

Father:
May your holy name
be honoured;
may your Kingdom
come.
Give us day by day
the food we need.
Forgive us our sins,
for we forgive
everyone who does
us wrong.
And do not bring us
to hard testing."'

'Thank you, Thomas,' said Mrs Hazel. 'So that is how Jesus wants us to pray. We think about God before we think about ourselves.'

Mrs Hazel opened her handbag. She took out the mobile phone.

'When Jesus prayed,' she said, 'he didn't just talk to God, his Father—he listened as well. It's rather like my mobile phone.

You can talk and you can listen. You can

also take it anywhere you go.

When we pray, we should listen to God and talk to him. We can pray anywhere—it doesn't have to be in church or at school.'

'Wish I'd got a mobile phone,' said Eleanor. 'Then I could talk to Kerry all the time.'

'I think it's probably just as well you haven't got one,' said Mrs Hazel, with a smile.

'For our prayer today we'll use the words Jesus taught us to say—the Lord's Prayer.'

After the prayer, they all drew a picture of Jesus with his friends.

Eleanor put a very small mobile phone in hers! You can see the painting Mrs Hazel chose if you look at the Big Frieze.

9. Donkeys are for peace

'Good morning, everyone,' said Mrs Foster. 'Today's assembly will be rather different from usual.'

It was Wednesday morning and the whole school was in the Big Hall. As a rule, the classes sat facing the front—one behind another. Today everything had changed. Some classes were on one side of the hall. They were facing the others on the other side. Between the two groups was a pathway. 2H were facing Mrs Jolley's Reception class.

There was something else different. Everybody was holding a green palm branch. The children had made them from sugar-paper the day before.

'Today we are thinking about a very special day in Jesus' life,' said Mrs Foster. 'It's the day we call Palm Sunday. It was the day when Jesus rode into the city of Jerusalem. 3G are going to lead our assembly and Amy will tell us the story.'

Amy from 3G stood up.

'One day, Jesus told his friends to fetch a donkey,' read Amy. 'He gave them a password in case they were stopped. "You must tell them that the Master needs it," said Jesus.'

Ben and Edward from 3G walked along the pathway between the classes. At the front of the hall they stopped. Sarah and Claire came over to them.

'Why are you untying our donkey?' they said.

'The Master needs it,' said Ben and Edward.

The two boys walked to the back of the hall.

'They took the donkey to Jesus,' read Amy. 'They put their cloaks on the donkey's back and helped Jesus get on. Jesus rode on the donkey and led the way into Jerusalem. His friends walked by him.'

All the children from 3G started to walk very slowly along the pathway between the other classes. Everyone stood up. They were holding their palm branches above their heads and waving them. Very soon everyone started to shout. The teachers joined in as well.

'God bless the king!'
'Praise God!'
'Peace in heaven and glory to God!'
'God bless the king!'

The shouting went on until the children
from 3G had reached the front of the hall.
Then everyone sat down.

'Jesus rode into Jerusalem on the day we
call Palm Sunday,' read Amy. 'If you go to
church on Palm Sunday, you will be given a
palm cross. This reminds people of that
special day.'

'Thank you, Amy, and all of 3G, for
leading our assembly today,' said Mrs Foster.

The children clapped 3G.

'You may think it rather strange that Jesus
rode a donkey,' said Mrs Foster.

'In those days, if a king rode a horse into a city, it meant war. If he rode a donkey, it meant he came in peace. Jesus came as king of love and peace. Jesus is the king of peace. The crowd loved him. They cheered and cheered, just like you. Now Sarah will read our prayer for us.'

Loving Father,
Thank you that Jesus came as King of Peace.
We pray that there may be:
peace in our hearts,
peace in our homes,
and peace in our world. Amen

'There's going to be lots of people on our new picture for the Big Frieze,' said Eleanor when 2H got back to their classroom.

And if you look, you can see that she was right.

10. Bread and wine

The children walked up Daisy Hill from the school to St John the Baptist church. They sat down in the choir seats near the big east window.

'It's really good to see you all here again,' said the vicar. 'Last time you came, we thought about baptism. We looked at the big window. Can anyone remember what the picture shows?'

'It was when Jesus was baptized,' said Mark.

'Well done,' said the vicar. 'Jesus was baptized by John before he started to tell people about God. Today we are going to think about something which happened towards the end of the time Jesus lived on earth.

Jesus knew that he would soon be returning to heaven. He wanted his friends to remember him in a very special way.'

The vicar pointed to what looked like a table with a cloth on it.

'Can you tell me what's on the altar?'

The altar stood under the big window.

'There's a sort of silver cup thing,' said Eleanor.

'And there's a silver plate,' added Jack.

'And a jug with water in it,' said Kerry.

'And one with wine,' said the vicar.

'And there's a slice of bread,' said Suzi.

'There's a white cloth,' said Donna.

'Good,' said the vicar. 'Now, if you saw these things on your table at home, what would you think might be going to happen?'

'We might be going to have a meal,' said Thomas. 'I don't think we'd get very much each, though!'

'Our table, or altar, is ready for a meal— a very special meal,' said the vicar. 'It's the special way by which Jesus wanted his friends to remember him. Jesus and his friends were all together in an upstairs room.'

The vicar lifted up the slice of bread.

'Jesus took some bread in his hands. He said a prayer and he gave each one of them a small piece.'

The vicar put the bread down. He poured some wine into the cup. He lifted up the cup.

'Jesus filled a cup with wine and prayed. Then he passed the cup to each of his friends in turn. They all had a sip of the wine. Today, two thousand years later, we still do this. We eat bread and drink wine and remember Jesus. Can anyone tell me what we call the service when we do this?'

'I think it's called Holy Communion,' said Donna.

'That's right,' said the vicar. 'It's "holy" because God is holy. It's "communion" because communion means being very close to someone. We are very close to Jesus in the Holy Communion service because we are doing what he told us to do.'

'But we can't all sit round that table,' said Eleanor.

'No,' said the vicar. 'Because it is holy— because it is God's meal—we usually kneel down to take the bread and wine. Perhaps Mrs Hazel will show us how we do it?'

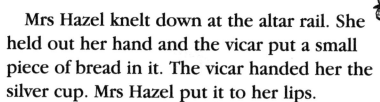

Mrs Hazel knelt down at the altar rail. She held out her hand and the vicar put a small piece of bread in it. The vicar handed her the silver cup. Mrs Hazel put it to her lips.

'As it's a very special meal, we eat and drink it in a special way,' said the vicar. 'It helps us to remember that it is Holy Communion.

Every Sunday and sometimes during the week we have a Holy Communion service in our church. Jesus left us something very wonderful to remember him by.'

'I think, before we go back to school, we'll ask the vicar to say our prayer for us,' said Mrs Hazel.

This is the prayer the vicar said.

Heavenly Father, thank you for sending Jesus to show us how to live. Thank you that, even though Jesus is holy, we can still be very close to him. Amen

'Thank you,' said Mrs Hazel to the vicar. 'Now, back to school. Be thinking about the Big Frieze as you go. We need a new picture for it.'

If you look hard, you can find out what they did.

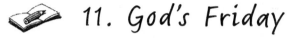

11. God's Friday

'It's ever so long,' said Mark. 'There are ten pictures now.'

'I like the one we did with the angel and shepherds and sheep,' said Kerry.

'I like the one with all the people in, that we did for Palm Sunday,' said Eleanor.

The children were looking at the Big Frieze.

'We have two more pictures to add to our Big Frieze,' said Mrs Hazel. 'One of them is a sad picture and one of them is a happy picture. The sad one comes first. Let's sit in the story corner and we'll talk about it.'

The children sat down. Thomas managed to beat Eleanor to the beanbag.

'The sad part of our story is about Jesus dying,' said Mrs Hazel. 'It happened on the day we call Good Friday. It sounds rather strange that we call it "Good" Friday. In the past it was sometimes called God's Friday and that probably became Good Friday. It was God's Friday because it was a very special day for Jesus. Can anyone tell me what happened to Jesus on Good Friday?'

'It was the day that Jesus died,' said Suzi. 'He died on a cross. My mum's got a little cross with Jesus on it.'

'That's right,' said Mrs Hazel. 'We call it a crucifix. Crucifix means "fixed to a cross". Can anyone tell me where we saw a crucifix not long ago?'

'I know,' said Donna. 'It was when we went to St John's church. There was a picture of one in that big window.'

'But I thought Jesus was good,' said Eleanor. 'If he was good, why did he die on a cross?'

'There were people who didn't like what Jesus was saying. They didn't like what Jesus was doing,' answered Mrs Hazel.

'They were the leaders of the Jewish people. They thought Jesus was wrong— that he was saying wrong things about God. They didn't believe that he was the Son of God. They didn't like the way that more people listened to Jesus than listened to them. They made up their minds to get rid of Jesus.'

'That's not fair,' said Eleanor. 'It's not fair at all.'

'No, it wasn't fair,' said Mrs Hazel. 'But the leaders of the Jewish people wanted to make sure that Jesus died. So Jesus was taken out of Jerusalem and put on a large wooden cross. It was a very sad day for all his friends. It was a very sad day for Mary, his mother, who was there. It was a very sad day for everyone.'

'So it wasn't a good Friday, was it?' asked Jack. 'We should really call it Sad Friday!'

'In one way, it was Sad Friday,' said Mrs Hazel.

'Sad because Jesus, who had done nothing wrong, had to die. But in another way, it was a good Friday. Christians believe that, because Jesus died, God will forgive us for the things we do wrong. Because Jesus died, we can be with him in heaven when we die.'

'That's what my mum told me when my great-nana died,' said Suzi. 'She told me that Great-Nana was in heaven with Jesus.'

The children were quiet for a moment after Suzi said that.

'So perhaps it was a good Friday after all,' said Mrs Hazel. 'After Jesus died, some friends buried his body. They took him off the cross. They carried him to a cave cut out of a hill. They laid Jesus inside.

A great big stone was rolled over the entrance to the cave.'

'But that can't be the end of the story!' said Eleanor. 'You promised us there was going to be a happy picture as well as a sad one.'

'Next time, we'll talk about our last picture,' said Mrs Hazel. 'But today we've thought about Good Friday—the day that Jesus died and was put into the cave. Now I'm going to read the verse of a hymn as our prayer.'

He died that we might *be* forgiven,
He died to make *us* good.
That we might go at last to heaven,
Saved *by* his precious blood. Amen

'Now we need a special picture for our Big Frieze.'

If you look carefully, you can see the picture Mrs Hazel chose.

12. An end and a beginning

'It was the sad bit last week,' said Eleanor. 'So it's the happy bit this week.'

Mrs Hazel laughed.

'Yes,' she said, 'we've come to the happy ending in the life of Jesus. There's only one more picture for our Big Frieze. Do you remember, when we started the story, we took the assembly for the whole school? We heard how the angel came to Mary.'

'I was Mary,' said Kerry.

'And I was Joseph,' said Thomas. 'I pretended I hit my thumb!'

'And you were the angel,' said Eleanor to Steven.

'Mrs Foster,' said Mrs Hazel, 'has asked us to tell the last part of the story—as Eleanor said, the "happy bit". We're going to do it in assembly next Wednesday.'

'Can I be in it this time?' asked Eleanor.

'I think everyone in the class will be in it,' said Mrs Hazel. 'Now let's talk about what happened.

Jesus was put in the cave on Good Friday. Early on Sunday morning, another Mary, not Jesus' mother, went to the cave.

When she got there, the big stone had been rolled away. This is a lovely part of the story and I would like us to act it. Before we do that, though, we need some scenery.'

Mrs Hazel gave 2H a big roll of corrugated paper.

They stretched it out and started to paint the hillside and the cave.

'We can pin this to the front of the stage in the Big Hall,' said Mrs Hazel.

Some of the children carried on with the painting. The others worked with Mrs Hazel and practised their parts in the play. By Wednesday morning, the scenery was dry and pinned to the stage.

Mrs Hazel stood at the front of the Big Hall. Eleanor walked on and stood in front of the big painting.

'On Easter Sunday morning,' said Mrs Hazel, 'Mary, one of Jesus' friends, went to the cave where Jesus had been taken. When she got there, the big stone had gone. She looked into the cave but Jesus wasn't there.'

Eleanor acted out the story as Mrs Hazel told it.

'Mary was very sad. She was crying because she thought someone had taken Jesus away. She was crying so hard that she couldn't see very well. Then Mary heard a voice. Through her tears she saw a man standing there. The man called out her name. "Mary," he said. It was Jesus. Mary could hardly believe it. Jesus wasn't dead. Jesus was alive.'

Eleanor didn't look sad any more. She ran off, shouting, 'He's alive! Jesus is alive!'

'On Easter Day, Jesus came back to life again,' said Mrs Hazel.

'During the next few weeks Jesus spoke to lots of his friends. He spoke to Peter and Andrew. He spoke to James and John. But the time was coming when Jesus had to go back to heaven to be with God, his Father. He told his friends to meet him on a hill overlooking Lake Galilee.'

All the children in 2H came on. They stood facing the stage.

'Before he left his friends, Jesus spoke to them,' said Mrs Hazel. 'Then Jesus was taken up to heaven until they could see him no longer.'

The children in 2H slowly lifted their heads. They waved their arms in the way that we do when we say goodbye to someone we love. They stood there very quietly.

'In one way, that is the end of our story of the life of Jesus,' said Mrs Hazel. 'In another, it is the start of another story. Peter and Andrew, James and John and all the others never forgot Jesus. They carried on

telling people about God—they tried to behave in the way that Jesus would have done, and they caught people for him. Those people caught others. That's why, two thousand years after Jesus went back to heaven, we can still learn about him today.'

'Thank you,' said Mrs Foster. 'A big thank you to 2H and Mrs Hazel. Just to remind us of what we've all been doing, 2H have brought their Big Frieze to show us.'

2H walked on again, holding their Big Frieze so that everyone in the school could see it. They had even put in their last picture. If you look, you can see what it is.

'Let's be quite quiet now for a few moments,' said Mrs Foster, 'and look at the Big Frieze. In the quiet, think about the life of Jesus. Then I will say a prayer.'

Lord Jesus, thank you for coming down to live on earth. Thank you for dying for us. Thank you for going back up to heaven so that we can know and love you today. Amen

Back in the classroom, the children were talking about the Big Frieze.

'I really liked doing that,' said Eleanor. 'Now I know lots more about Jesus.'

Bible passages used in Downs and Ups at Daisy Hill School

1. Messages: The annunciation
Luke 1:26–56 and Matthew 1:18–25

2. Mary's baby: The birth of Jesus; shepherds and wise men
Luke 2:1–20 and Matthew 2:1–14

3. Not lost—just missing: The boy Jesus in the temple
Luke 2:41–52

4. Promises: The baptism of Jesus
Matthew 3:13–17

5. There's people to be caught: Jesus chooses his friends
Matthew 4:18–22

6. Ear today and gone tomorrow: Jesus tells a story
Matthew 13:1–9

7. Now open your eyes: Jesus heals Bartimaeus
Mark 10:46–52

8. Two-way talking: Jesus teaches his friends to pray
Luke 11:1–4

9. Donkeys are for peace: Jesus rides into Jerusalem
Luke 19:28–40

10. Bread and wine: The Last Supper
Luke 22:14–20 and 1 Corinthians 11:23–26

11. God's Friday: The death of Jesus
Luke 23:50–56

12. An end and a beginning: The resurrection and ascension of Jesus
John 20:11–23 and Acts 1:6–11

More from Brian Ogden

Special Days at Daisy Hill School

The Church Year for young readers

There are a number of special days spread throughout the year, most of which are based on the life of Jesus. And today is a special day for Class 2H at Daisy Hill School. 'Today,' says their teacher, Mrs Hazel, 'is the beginning of our new topic on special days.'

There's so much to do and so much to learn. There are two huge friezes to be made. And there is a 'Special Days' clock, with spaces for the names of twelve special days and lots of pictures.

You too can join in the fun and discover that special days are more than just Christmas and Easter!

ORDER FORM				
REF	TITLE	PRICE	QTY	TOTAL
139 8	Special Days at Daisy Hill School	£3.99		

POSTAGE & PACKING CHARGES			
Order value	UK	Postage and packing:	
£7.00 & under	£1.25	Donation:	
£7.01–£30.00	£2.50		
Over £30.00	free	**Total enclosed:**	

Name _____ Account Number _____

Address _____

_____ Postcode _____

Telephone Number _____ Email _____

Payment by: Cheque ❏ Mastercard ❏ Visa ❏ Postal Order ❏ Switch ❏

Credit card no. ❏❏❏❏ ❏❏❏❏ ❏❏❏❏ ❏❏❏❏ Expires ❏❏ ❏❏

Switch card no. ❏❏❏❏❏❏❏❏❏❏❏❏❏❏❏❏❏❏

Issue no. of Switch card ❏❏❏❏ Expires ❏❏ ❏❏

Signature _____ Date _____

All orders must be accompanied by the appropriate payment.

Please send your completed order form to:
BRF, Peter's Way, Sandy Lane West, Oxford OX4 5HG
Tel. 01865 748227 / Fax. 01865 773150 Email: enquiries@brf.org.uk

Available from your local Christian bookshop.   BRF is a Registered Charity